ANGLING FOR WORDS

BASIC ANGLING PRACTICE BOOK

Student Book

Revised Edition

Dorothy B. Montgomery
Linda M. Gipson

Decoding and Spelling Practice with Basic Vocabulary

Academic Therapy Publications
Novato, California

Academic Therapy Publications
20 Leveroni Court
Novato, California 94949

International Standard Book Number: 0-87879-518-9
22 21 20 19
15 14 13 12 11 10 09

ISBN: 0-87879-518-9
ISBN 13: 978-0-87879-518-5

TABLE OF CONTENTS

TABLE OF CONTENTS (CONT.)

TABLE OF CONTENTS (CONT.)

CONCERNING THE TEACHER'S MANUAL OF *BASIC ANGLING PRACTICE BOOK*

The following aids for the instructor are to be found in the Teacher's Manual, the supplement to this book:

– Introductory information and detailed instructions about using this material as a program or supplement

– Instructional commentary for the use of each page for reading and/or spelling

– Sample lesson plan

– Instructions, key, and marking charts for the *Basic Angling* "Phonetic Skills Survey"

– "Trophy" progress chart and its key for reading

– Spelling Curriculum Chart

– Spelling Curriculum Record Chart and key

– Supplementary functional word lists

– List of compatible supplementary materials

ORDER OF INTRODUCTION OF LEARNED WORDS

Basic Angling
Phonetic Skills Survey

Ia.	nit	Ib.	shum
	las		thap
	fep		chog
	hom		whib
	kud		heth
	vib		rutch
	weff		quid
	cax		
	yog	Ic.	semping
	juz		doffy
			cadly
Ib.	dron		bitted
	glit		gupped
	smup		lanter
	crad		med's
	beld		hoxes
	hist		pindle
	fomp		raspet
	keck		grudsip
	runk		plinglit
	jang		ferrin

Phonetic Skills Survey (cont.)

II.		III.		IV.	
	ne		leet		gon
	ble		vean		gep
	habe		boof		lage
	vike		gaip		
	rofe		zay	V.	bo´
	mune		noad		re´
	dete		soe		fu´
	sype		roul		savel
	nare		pow		nipan
	luse		daw		pulit
			taun		joble
	cet		jall		tapa
	cag		hoy		
	cid		coip	VI.	fadge
	cos				wam
	cyl	IV.	pler		kew
	hiled		stur		lation
	pold		smir		
	kigh		tror		
			clar		

Short a (ă)

1. | fat | bat | mat | sat |
ran	tan	pan	can
nap	lap	sap	map
tag	rag	bag	gag

2. | sad | mad | dad | lad |
ham	Sam	ram	am
tab	lab	jab	cab
fan	an	Dan	van

3. | pat | cat | at | hat |
bad	had	pad	Dad
tap	rap	cap	gap
pal	man	gas	rat

4. | fat ham | sad man | mad lad |
tan bat	bad cat	had gas
am sad	cab ran	Dan sat
can pat	rag mat	map bag

****

5. | han | fam | bap | taf |
las	sab	gat	cam
rad	dag	jav	nac
paf	lat	dap	mas

Short i (ĭ)

1. hit   bit   fit   it
    dim   him   rim   Kim
    rip   sip   tip   nip
    hid   rid   lid   kid

2. big   fig   rig   pig
    tin   sin   pin   fin
    did   mid   Sid   bid
    rib   bib   lip   dip

3. hit   lip   sip   bin
    hid   lid   sit   bit
    bid   rid   pit   kit
    big   rim   pig   kin
    dig   him   fig   pin
    dip   hip   fin   din

4. tin lid   hit him   sip it
    big rim   it fit   sit in
    tip him   did pin   if lit

****

5. bif   mip   lig   ris
    min   tib   nid   sif
    hig   rin   dis   nil

2

Short <u>a</u> and <u>i</u>

1. hid   bat   pin   dam
   had   bit   pan   dim
2. lap   him   tip   bag
   lip   ham   tap   big

3. bin   rag   fan   did
   ban   rig   fin   dad
4. nip   mad   bid   sit
   nap   mid   bad   sat

5. lad   sip   pat   tin
   lid   sap   pit   tan
6. fat   in   sad   at
   fit   an   Sid   it

7. big pad   tan lid   cap fit
   rat hid   kid him   ram it
8. Sam had a bad pig. It bit Dan.
   A rag had a rip. It had a pin.

****

9. sim   min   lig   tas
   pab   lan   rin   dif
   rit   nad   hib   dap
   sal   tif   mag   bic

Final s and Plurals

S(z) at the end of short words, plurals, and verbs:

1.
as	is	bags	cans
tabs	figs	kids	pads
dims	rags	cabs	fins
gags	bibs	hams	lids
rids	pals	pigs	vans
tags	sins	labs	digs

S(s) at the end of present verbs and plurals:

2.
tips	mats	hits	laps
bats	rips	cats	fits
naps	sits	pats	nips
lips	gaps	bits	caps

1. A big man hits Sid.
2. A tin can fits in a bag.
3. Nan has a pin in a cap.
4. Tim pats his cat.
5. Fat pigs had a nap.
6. A rat digs in a dam.
7. Is a ram as fat as a pig?
8. Jim can bat as Van did.
9. His pal tips a bat at him.
10. Pam sits in a big lab.

Short <u>u</u> (ŭ)

1. | but | hut | nut | rut |
    |------|------|------|------|
    | sun | bun | run | fun |
    | tug | rug | mug | hug |
    | hum | sum | gum | mum |

2. | rub | tub | cub | hub |
    |------|------|------|------|
    | mud | bud | dud | suds |
    | up | cup | sup | pup |
    | cut | gun | bug | dug |

3. | nut | pub | but | fun |
    |------|------|------|------|
    | nub | tub | cut | run |
    | rub | tug | cup | rug |
    | rum | pug | sup | bug |
    | sum | hug | pup | bum |
    | sub | hut | pun | hum |

4. | jugs | cuts | sums | tubs |
    |------|------|------|------|
    | nuts | buds | runs | cups |
    | hums | guns | pups | bugs |

****

5. | tup | nud | cum | duf |
    |------|------|------|------|
    | pum | lun | nug | hus |
    | rud | bup | mun | sul |

Final Double Consonants

1.

miss	dill	cuff	add
dull	tiff	lass	inn
mass	hull	puff	till
bill	hiss	fill	mitt

2.

fuss	miff	pill	kiss
hill	pass	muss	Jill
muff	sill	bass	putt

****

3.

tass	rill	caff	niss
diff	biss	vill	laff
nass	kiff	dass	riff

1. Jill is a sad lass.
2. Can a cab pass a van?
3. Dan has a pill in his cup.
4. Jan hits Pat in a fuss.
5. Fill up a tin can.
6. A pup dug up a hill.
7. A bass has fins.
8. A lad can muss up his bib.
9. Did Sam miss a sum?

Short e (ĕ)

1.
fed	led	red	bed
men	pen	ten	hen
get	met	let	set
peg	leg	beg	keg

2.
den	Len	Ben	Ken
jell	bell	sell	fell
mess	less	Bess	egg
Nell	tell	Jeff	Les

3.
get	beg	pen	dell
let	bed	pet	sell
led	Ted	bet	set
leg	ten	bell	met

4.
lag	den	pet	lid
lug	Dan	pit	led
leg	din	pat	lad

5.
red tag	fed ham	hen sets
bad bet	peg leg	sell pets

****

6.
nev	res	hed	lec
dem	pel	jes	sen

7

Short Vowel Discrimination

1. peg   red   sit   hem
    pig   rid   set   him
    big   led   let   bid
    beg   lid   lit   bed

2. lad   ten   mid   mutt
    led   tin   mud   mat
    lid   tan   mad   met

3. fell   mass   sill   bell
    fill   mess   sell   bill

4. sad   kin   den   gun
    lip   bed   fuss   ten
    cub   jag   rap   hid
    red   hum   fig   cap

Initial w

5. wet   will   wed   wag
    wig   web   well   win
    red wig   big win   wet rag
    run well   pet wags   Nan will

Add Learned words: <u>the</u>, <u>go</u>, <u>he</u>, <u>of</u>, <u>to</u>

1. A lid fell in the tin can.
2. Sam will fuss at the mess.
3. Jud tips a pan. The pups nip it.
4. Go get the red hen in the pen.
5. Jeff can sell caps at the hut.
6. Bud has a can of ham in his cab.
7. Ted fell in the mud. Dad is mad.
8. Let the big cats sit in the van.
9. Pat met a cub in its den.
10. Jan is at the pass in the hills.
11. Ben taps his bell. It is fun.
12. Bill hid his pill in the bed.
13. His bat is wet. It will miss.
14. Ted set his legs in the keg.

Initial Consonant <u>y</u>

yes   yam   yell   yet

1. Len yells at the man in the van.
2. He is big, yet he let Kit go.
3. Yes, the lad will run to the hut.
4. The ten pigs dug up the yams.

Short o (ŏ)

1.
hop	mop	top	cop
mob	sob	cob	Bob
tot	not	hot	lot
cod	pod	rod	God

2.
got	dot	pot	rot
rob	gob	lob	job
log	dog	jog	cog
pop	bop	lop	sop

3.
mob	tot	rod	mom
cob	dot	nod	Tom
cot	dog	nog	Tod
lot	log	bog	sod
lop	lob	bop	sop
top	rob	mop	cop

4.
cut	tag	sod	lot
cat	tug	sad	let
cot	togs	suds	lit

5.
log rots	wet mop	rob a cop
on a pod	hot rod	tug a cot
in a bog	bad job	odd doll

10

Final <u>x</u> (ks)

mix	fox	wax	tux
ox	tax	six	box
sax	fix	ax	sex

<u>z</u> Words

zip	buzz	fizz	zap
jazz	fuzz	Oz	zips

Add Learned Word: <u>I</u>, <u>you</u>

1. The fox had its cubs in the den.
2. The cat will hop to the log.
3. The top of a box fell on the rug.
4. I will not go if you will fuss.
5. Jed cut the tag off of the box.
6. He did get a job in the pit.
7. Can you fix the van? I am hot.
8. Six pigs dug up a sod hill.
9. Tex had an ax to cut the log.
10. You can wax the top well.
11. The bugs buzz in the hot sun.
12. I am not a tot. I can sell a lot.

Short Vowel Discrimination

1.

fan	rot	tug	sag
fin	got	tag	sap
fun	get	bag	sop
run	let	big	pop
ran	leg	wig	pep
Ron	lug	wag	peg

2.

web	hen	gum	lip
wet	ten	sum	lop
met	tin	Sam	Lon
mat	pin	sad	lob
man	pun	Sid	lab
men	gun	sip	jab

3.

jell	pot	hog	ram
tell	pet	hop	jam
till	net	hip	Jim
dill	nut	dip	Jill
doll	hut	dim	will
dot	hug	rim	well

4.

job	Nat	rut	dog
jab	net	rug	bog
nab	nut	dug	beg

Practice Sentences

1. A big web is in the tub.
2. Ben will yell if Sam wins.
3. Nell cuts the red wig on the doll.
4. Can a yam bud in the mud?
5. The pup is wet in the suds.

6. A dog will yap at the big bugs.
7. The cut on his lip is well.
8. Let Ned sit in the pit to dig.
9. Will the vans pass in the rut?
10. Can Sam wed the miss?   Yes!

11. Jeff sits on gum.   It is a mess.
12. It is a lot of fun to hop to you.
13. Six men tug at the big box.
14. Can you go to the top of a hill?
15. Dad lets the lad sit in his van.

16. Mom will mop but not wax.
17. Bob can fix the rip in the cot.
18. A red fox runs at the fat ox.
19. The tot sobs a lot.   Hug him.
20. Tod has a job in a cab.   Get in!
21. Dot sets a rag on the tan bag.

Short a Blends

1. lap   lam   lag   lad
   clap   slam   flag   glad

2. tag   tab   nap   rag
   stag   stab   snap   drag

3. rap   lap   ram   lan
   trap   slap   cram   plan

4. slap   gram   flat   glad
   brag   flap   crab   snag
   clam   bran   trap   scab
   snap   drag   clap   brad

5. gas   ban   ram   pan
   gasp   band   ramp   pant

6. lamp   damp   camp   ramp
   hand   land   sand   band
   fast   mast   past   cast
   ask   task   mask   bask

7. had crab   gas lamp   rat trap
   last bat   camp map   flat pan

Short i Blends

1.   lid   rim   rip   lip
          slid   trim   drip   clip

2.   rim   lit   rim   pin
          grim   flit   prim   spin

3.   nip   rip   lit   rib
          snip   trip   slit   crib

4.   limp   silk   risk   list
          milk   drip   lint   gift
          film   sift   slip   brig
          grip   trim   flip   grit

5.   dip   sit   lit   tip
          drip   spit   lint   trip

6.   slap   fist   clam   spin
          drill   brass   grab   skim
          snap   still   flat   past
          cliff   trim   ramp   flap
          grin   crab   miss   lamp
          plan   sniff   slit   raft
          blast   flint   clip   gill

Short <u>u</u> Blends

1.   pun   mug   rum   lug
     spun   smug   drum   plug

2.   rug   nub   lug   tub
     drug   snub   slug   stub

3.   bus   bum   Gus   rum
     bust   bump   gust   rump

4.   plum   grub   slum   spun
     club   smug   drug   scum
     bump   must   pump   rust
     gulp   tuft   bulb   jump

5.   pug   sun   gut   cub
     plug   stun   glut   club

6.   brag   stub   glum   skin
     drip   span   list   stab
     pulp   gift   just   band
     lint   past   film   hump

7.   stump grill   draft   skull
     plant   bluff   stunt   clamp

Practice

1. clap hands   past the stump
2. trap a fox   spin a top
3. plan the trip   damp rags
4. fast jump   grab the pig
5. ask the man   on the grill

6. Snip the top of the plant.
7. Will you jump from a cliff?
8. The wet mop drips on the rug.
9. Jill sets the doll in the crib.
10. The lad gulps a glass of milk.

11. Will you grin if you get a gift?
12. Ed ran past the hut to a stump.
13. Sam stabs a pin in his skin.
14. The van hit a bump on the hill.
15. A plum fell in a gust of wind.

16. Brad must not drag his bat.
17. The bulb in the lamp is dim.
18. Stan lugs the drum up the ramp.
19. The dog did a flip at his stunt.
20. I will go on a raft trip at camp.
21. Ben grips the plug in his fist.

Short e Blends

1. led   red   led   led
    fled   bred   sled   bled

2. ten   men   Ben   den
    tent   mend   bent   dent

3. step   Greg   sped   clef
    fret   stem   tent   end
    help   desk   pest   rent
    sent   jest   bend   melt
    lend   belt   rest   went
    bent   west   tend   best
    vest   dent   held   test

4. bed   set   sell   net
    bend   sent   spell   nest

5. bet   let   pet   wet
    best   lent   pest   went

6. dress   swell   press   spent
    smell   trend   slept   blend
    spend   swept   blest   sleds
    cleft   bless   dwell   crest

Short o Blends

1.   rod   lot   top   cot
        trod   clot   stop   Scot

2.   lot   rot   rod   lop
        plot   trot   prod   flop

3.   log   top   cot   pod
        clog   stop   cost   plod

4.   drop   spot   smog   flop
        slot   trod   prom   stop
        blot   flog   plot   clod
        crop   slop   loft   soft
        fond   pond   bond   romp
        doll   moss   boss   loss
        floss   blond   lost   toss

5.   cost a lot   stop the plot
6.   blot a spot   clog the pond
7.   stop drills   a blond doll
8.   a soft rag   moss in a pond
9.   crop wilts   hens in a loft
10.   in the slot   toss the film
11.   trots fast   mops up spills

Initial Blends (Real and Nonsense)

1.
brat	crat	drat	frat
bret	cret	dret	fret
brit	crit	drit	frit
brot	crot	drot	frot
brut	crut	drut	frut

2.
grat	prat	trat	blat
gret	pret	tret	blet
grit	prit	trit	blit
grot	prot	trot	blot
grut	prut	trut	blut

3.
clat	flat	glat	plat
clet	flet	glet	plet
clit	flit	glit	plit
clot	flot	glot	plot
clut	flut	glut	plut

4.
scat	sket	skit	Scot
slat	slet	slit	slot
smat	smet	smit	smot
snat	snet	snit	snut
spat	spet	spit	spot
stat	stet	stit	stut

Final Blends (Real and Nonsense)

1.
bast	dast	rast	tast
best	dest	rest	test
bist	dist	rist	tist
bost	dost	rost	tost
bust	dust	rust	tust

2.
bant	mant	hant	sant
bent	ment	hent	sent
bint	mint	hint	sint
bont	mont	hont	sont
bunt	munt	hunt	sunt

3.
daft	laft	raft	taft
deft	left	reft	teft
dift	lift	rift	tift
doft	loft	roft	toft
duft	luft	ruft	tuft

4.
bask	nask	pask	vask
besk	nesk	pesk	vesk
bisk	nisk	pisk	visk
bosk	nosk	posk	vosk
busk	nusk	pusk	vusk

Mixed Blends

1. | cliff | raft | crust | wept |
   |-------|------|-------|------|
   | stand | plump | swift | draft |
   | brisk | flint | tramp | stump |
   | spill | graft | print | twist |

2. | blast | still | grass | tusk |
   |-------|-------|-------|------|
   | stiff | brand | trust | plant |
   | lumps | class | stamp | slump |
   | strip | stress | split | strap |

1. Ask Bob if he has a grill.
2. The sun will melt the soft wax.
3. Rub the brass on the lamp.
4. The fog and smog kept us in.
5. You must grip the tin clamps.
6. I cut grass and trim stems.
7. Print and spell at the desk.
8. Jill let the damp rag drip.
9. It is best not to gulp milk.
10. The tot slept in a big crib.
11. The belt of the dress is lost.
12. Bill felt his pants split.
13. Bend and clasp hands if you can.
14. Greg sent the cubs to the tent.

<u>ck</u> Words

1. | | | | |
    |---|---|---|---|
    | pick | tack | neck | tuck |
    | deck | kick | suck | lack |
    | rock | duck | tick | sack |
    | luck | mock | pack | wick |
    | sick | rack | Rick | sock |
    | back | lick | dock | buck |

2. | | | | |
    |---|---|---|---|
    | truck | click | stack | fleck |
    | flick | stock | pluck | clock |
    | crock | smack | speck | crack |
    | slack | flock | brick | black |
    | trick | track | block | stuck |

Add Learned Words: <u>there</u>, <u>come</u>, <u>are</u>

1. He fell on the deck of the raft.
2. There is a spot on his back.
3. The truck will come up the ramp.
4. Stack the rocks on the track.
5. The ducks are on top of a cliff.
6. Ron got sick and went to bed.
7. There are cracks in the clock.
8. The frogs come to the dock.

nk Words

1.
sink	rank	bunk	ink
bank	link	honk	sunk
pink	sank	mink	wink
tank	rink	hunk	lank
kink	Hank	dank	punk

2.
drank	skunk	stink	flunk
spunk	flank	drunk	drink
plank	brink	spank	trunk

ng Words

3.
hang	lung	sing	fang
sung	rang	bang	hung
long	sang	song	ring
sting	slang	bring	clang

1. His pet skunk drank from the cup.
2. There are songs I can sing well.
3. Mom will spank Dan if he yells.
4. The ducks are in the long tank.
5. A big clang comes from the bell.

<u>sh</u> Words

1.
shop	shin	shut	shed
ship	shot	shag	shun
shall	shift	shell	shelf
sham	shock	shuck	shack
shrimp	shrank	shrub	shrink

2.
rash	hush	dish	mesh
gush	dash	lash	rush
mash	wish	cash	fish

3.
brush	flash	slush	crash
flesh	plush	fresh	blush
trash	crush	flush	swish
clash	slash	slosh	smash

1. The ships are at the big dock.
2. The truck will crush the trash.
3. I wish to pass the next test.
4. He has a rash and will not come.
5. The men shot ducks at the pond.
6. I shall not smash the rocks.
7. Fresh shrimp are in pink shells.
8. There are fish in the mesh nets.

<u>th</u> (th) Words

1. thin   thank   thing   think
    thud   thick   thump   thongs
    theft   thug   thrill   throb

2. bath   moth   path   with
    tenth   fifth   width   length

<u>th</u> (th) Words

this   that   then   them
thus   than

1. That is the tenth man to come in.
2. The belt of his pants is thin.
3. Jon went on a path that is fresh.
4. Brush the moth off this shelf.
5. The thrill of the test is to win.
6. The tot will slosh in his bath.
7. He cut the width of the shrub.
8. You must think you can run fast.
9. I went with them to the shop.
10. It fell with a thump and a thud.
11. The flesh of his neck throbs.

<u>ch</u> (ch) Words

1.
chop	chap	chip	chug
chat	chin	chum	chick
chill	chess	chunk	champ
check	chuck	chock	chest

2.
lunch	bench	punch	rich
ranch	bunch	inch	such
pinch	gulch	branch	crunch

Final <u>tch</u> (ch)

1.
| match | pitch | fetch | witch |
| notch | catch | itch | batch |

2.
hitch	ditch	patch	clutch
snatch	crutch	twitch	sketch
	stitch	stretch	

1. Patch the dress with pink felt.
2. I shall chop the bench with an ax.
3. He has a lunch box in his desk.
4. Bob fell on his back in the ditch.

wh (hw) Words

whip	when	whack	which
whet	whiz	whiff	whisk

1. When Russ is ill, he is cross.
2. Which of the dogs can catch him?
3. He has a whip that is split.
4. Get a whiff of that strong smell!
5. Jeff will whack him with his fist.
6. His cab can whiz on a fast track.

qu (kw) Words

quick	quiz	quack	quilt
quest	quill	squid	squelch

1. A quick trip to the club is fun.
2. The ink of the quill pen is black.
3. The big squid had ten long legs.
4. Ducks quack and swim in ponds.
5. There is a quilt on the twin bed.
6. A quiz is a test that is not long.

Suffix -<u>ing</u>

1. sanding   bumping   risking
    helping   romping   bending
    rusting   milking   lumping
    wilting   testing   casting

2. pressing   drifting   blasting
    sniffing   clamping   flossing
    branding   grilling   smelling
    swelling   stomping   grafting

3. dimming   napping   running
    begging   tipping   getting
    patting   humming   jabbing
    kidding   robbing   cutting

4. grinning   plugging   stabbing
    stepping   clotting   trimming
    drumming   snapping   sledding

1. Pam is lending Fran a black vest.
2. I am running on the fast track.
3. Jon is telling his dad the trick.
4. The tot is not spilling his milk.

Vowel y (ĭ) Words

Suffix y on base words:

1.
dusty	hilly	fishy	grassy
milky	bulky	sandy	flashy
lumpy	drafty	messy	mushy
filmy	smelly	crusty	bumpy
fussy	chilly	fluffy	dressy

Suffix y on doubled consonant:

2.
choppy	baggy	sunny	foggy
gritty	spotty	leggy	gummy
shaggy	nutty	chatty	floppy
runny	skinny	muddy	witty

1. The lad fell on the bumpy path.
2. A shaggy dog is romping with him.
3. Sam is messy from the muddy pit.
4. Pants are baggy on his skinny legs.
5. A pond is choppy when it is windy.
6. Mom is sitting in a chilly draft.
7. I am sledding on a grassy hill.
8. The fussy tot is begging to go.

Suffix -ly (lĭ)

1. dimly   madly   fitly
   sadly   hotly   manly
   flatly   trimly   smugly

2. grimly   lastly   costly
   fondly   thinly   gladly
   justly   softly   primly

3. stiffly   gruffly   crossly
   blackly   sickly   rashly
   richly   freshly   thickly
   quickly   grandly   crisply

Add Learned Words: Mr., Mrs., said

1. Mr. Black went quickly to bed.
2. I will gladly send you a gift.
3. He thinks you are acting badly.
4. Jim sat stiffly on the bench.
5. Pat said sadly that Bob is ill.
6. Mr. Brent acts crossly a lot.
7. It is costly to go to the track.
8. Tom said flatly that he will go.

31

Suffix -ed (ĕd)

Suffix -ed (ĕd) after final t:

1.
rested	hunted	acted
bunted	rented	punted
lifted	panted	tested

2.
shifted	trusted	slanted
stunted	melted	dusted
printed	rusted	drifted

Suffix -ed (ĕd) after final d:

3.
handed	ended	bonded
mended	sanded	added
branded	blended	landed

Suffix -ed (ĕd) on doubled t or d:

4.
padded	kidded	batted
rotted	petted	sodded
fitted	lidded	rutted

5.
slotted	fitted	plodded
fretted	prodded	clotted

Suffix -ed (t)

1.
missed	packed	bossed
helped	jumped	sacked
ticked	messed	pumped
backed	winked	yanked

2.
spanked	blocked	scuffed
bluffed	stacked	thanked
glassed	slumped	blinked
plucked	frisked	stamped

3.
clinked	scoffed	flunked
grasped	flicked	tracked
stumped	cranked	dressed
tricked	pressed	shucked

1. The lad packed a bag and dressed.
2. He then kissed his mom and left.
3. A frog jumped in the pond to swim.
4. Pat helped Jan fix the fresh fish.
5. I tacked the list on the plank.
6. The clock on the shelf ticked.
7. Ben stacked the box next to a van.
8. Dan spanked Tom with a flat brush.

Suffix -ed (d)

1. hanged   killed   jelled
    filmed   dulled   banged
    longed   yelled   billed

2. filled   smelled   drilled
    spelled   chilled   shelled
    thrilled   clanged   grilled

Suffix -ed on doubled consonant:

3. gunned   rammed   rigged
    tagged   hummed   dinned
    sobbed   begged   jogged
    canned   robbed   tugged

4. slammed   grinned   plugged
    stubbed   grabbed   clogged
    stemmed   drugged   stabbed
    planned   trimmed   drummed

1. Beth filled the cup with hot milk.
2. He grinned as he grabbed the ring.
3. Dad yelled when he banged his leg.

Suffix -er (ẽr)

Suffix -er meaning "a person who":

1.   helper   kicker   banker
       singer   golfer   speller
       hunter   driller   jumper
       lender   packer   blocker

2.   passer   spender   printer
       rancher   pitcher   catcher
       checker   drinker   renter
       stacker   pincher   camper

Suffix -er meaning "a thing which":

3.   mixer   hanger   bumper
       rocker   cracker   sheller
       tracker   thriller   puncher
       duster   blender   pumper

Suffix -er meaning "more":

4.   longer   richer   faster
       plumper   blacker   stiffer
       softer   damper   stronger

Suffix Practice

Add Learned Words: <u>here</u>, <u>look</u>, <u>was</u>

1. The hunter tracked the swift elk.
2. The pitcher bunted the fast pitch.
3. He looked sadly at his bent bumper.
4. Mr. Smith went in a rented camper.
5. A rancher sniffed a strong smell.
6. Mrs. Black was sitting in a rocker.
7. Tom grasped the string and yanked.
8. He yelled from the steps at Ben.

Contractions or Possessives -<u>s</u>

1.	can't	isn't	hasn't	it's
2.	let's	you'd	I'll	he's
3.	I'm	he'll	I'd	you'll
4.	Bob's	cat's	Ken's	man's

1. The dog's leg limped as he ran.
2. I'm pressing a mussed dress.
3. He'll pitch longer than Sam did.
4. Can't you gladly thank Tom's dad?

Suffix -es (ĕz)

Plural or present verb suffix after s, x, z, ch, sh:

1. | dresses | bosses | glasses |
   |---------|--------|---------|
   | misses | fusses | kisses |
   | passes | blesses | tosses |
   | presses | flosses | classes |

2. | taxes | sixes | boxes |
   |-------|-------|-------|
   | fixes | waxes | tuxes |
   | sexes | mixes | axes |

3. | buzzes | fizzes | fuzzes |
   |--------|--------|--------|

4. | riches | punches | inches |
   |--------|---------|--------|
   | ranches | benches | pinches |

5. | matches | witches | notches |
   |---------|---------|---------|
   | sketches | stitches | patches |
   | itches | clutches | batches |

6. | dishes | rashes | wishes |
   |--------|--------|--------|
   | smashes | crushes | mashes |
   | blushes | sloshes | brushes |

Consonant le Words

	-ble	-dle	-tle
1.	fumble	candle	bottle
2.	ramble	toddle	rattle
3.	crumble	saddle	little
4.	gamble	huddle	settle
5.	hobble	middle	cattle
6.	pebble	fiddle	kettle

	-ple	-gle	-fle
1.	apple	wiggle	ruffle
2.	dimple	single	raffle
3.	topple	straggle	muffle
4.	sample	angle	sniffle
5.	ripple	struggle	baffle

1. He's got an apple that's crunchy.
2. Bob had a dimple on his chin.
3. That rat wiggles from Mom's trap.
4. Bill fell on a gritty pebble.
5. The candles in the boxes melted.
6. Jan sat in the saddle stiffly.

Consonant le Practice

1. bundle   stumble   tackle
    cripple   handle   bubble
    pickle   simple   juggle
    mumble   paddle   freckle

Consonant le Words with -ed:

2. fiddled   sampled   sniffled
    rattled   trickled   bundled
    grumbled   settled   tackled
    giggled   huddled   nibbled

1. Nan wishes to tickle Dot's back.
2. A kicker left the huddle quickly.
3. The winning runner stumbled badly.
4. Cattle on ranches look well fed.
5. Sand shifted and the hill toppled.
6. He punches notches in his saddle.
7. Tim blocked the punt and tackled.
8. Come here and help with the dishes.
9. The golfer was inches from a win.
10. The kettle rattled as I grabbed it.

Compound Words

Short <u>a</u> and <u>i</u>

1.
anthill	dishpan	flapjack
kingfish	windmill	pickax
sandbag	milkman	slapstick
pigskin	catfish	rattrap
handbag	lipstick	handclasp
madman	ragbag	dipstick

Short <u>a</u>, <u>i</u>, <u>u</u>, <u>e</u>

2.
sunhat	redskin	handcuff
wetback	sickbed	backrest
himself	hubcap	nutshell
busman	dustpan	freshman
sunset	itself	shellfish

1. A little rat was in the rattrap.
2. At sunset the windmill stopped.
3. The milkman clutches his bottles.
4. A red hubcap was in the ditch.
5. Set the lipstick on the dresser.
6. A frog sunned himself on a rock.

Compound Words

Short a, i, u, e, o

1. hilltop   flagship   backpack
   pickup   sundeck   padlock
   dishrag   wingspan   handbill
   sunlamp   millpond   chessman

2. sandbox   stopgap   backdrop
   cockpit   pillbox   shotgun
   backstop   hotbed   lunchbox
   potluck   cannot   checkup
   codfish   drumstick   matchbox

1. Jan has a lunchbox with a bottle.
2. I left the dishrag on the shelf.
3. The catcher was at the backstop.
4. Shotgun shells cost a lot.
5. The wingspan of a gull is long.
6. Mrs. Slack just had a checkup.
7. His lunch was in his backpack.
8. The hot sunlamp was left on.
9. A drummer dropped his drumstick.
10. Bob had a catnap on the sundeck.

VC′/CV Words – Short <u>a</u> - <u>i</u>

1.
nap kin	fab ric	vic tim
mam mal	at tic	sig nal
pic nic	rab bit	can vas
san dal	kid nap	zig zag

2.
at las	van dal	plas tic
ras cal	ban dit	bal lad
tid bit	man tis	ban tam

VC′/CV Words <u>a</u>, <u>i</u>, <u>u</u>

3.
muf fin	tal cum	pub lic
cac tus	hic cup	cam pus
sum mit	al bum	sin ful
pab lum	sun lit	cat sup

VC′/CV Words – <u>a</u>, <u>i</u>, <u>u</u>, <u>e</u>

4.
sud den	tab let	mal let
cas ket	kit ten	nut meg
vel vet	cut let	ten nis
pup pet	fat ten	nug get
hel met	bas ket	rid den
pel let	hid den	pal let

VC´/CV Words – Short <u>a</u> - <u>i</u>

1. | | | |
   |---|---|---|
   | rabbit | canvas | napkin |
   | zigzag | mammal | fabric |
   | victim | kidnap | sandal |
   | picnic | attic | signal |

2. | | | |
   |---|---|---|
   | bandit | plastic | tidbit |
   | rascal | ballad | mantis |
   | bantam | atlas | vandal |

VC´/CV Words <u>a</u>, <u>i</u>, <u>u</u>

3. | | | |
   |---|---|---|
   | hiccup | sinful | campus |
   | pablum | muffin | album |
   | catsup | public | sunlit |
   | summit | cactus | talcum |

VC´/CV Words – <u>a</u>, <u>i</u>, <u>u</u>, <u>e</u>

4. | | | |
   |---|---|---|
   | tennis | puppet | mallet |
   | casket | kitten | nutmeg |
   | hidden | pallet | ridden |
   | tablet | sudden | velvet |
   | cutlet | fatten | nugget |
   | helmet | basket | pellet |

VC´/CV Words

1. | ribbon | happen | tinsel |
    |---------|--------|---------|
    | button | seldom | magnet |
    | goblin | absent | lesson |
    | custom | metric | bonnet |

2. | mitten | common | gallon |
    |---------|---------|---------|
    | combat | goblet | mascot |
    | mantel | dentist | possum |
    | bottom | tonsil | cannon |

1. I ran to the summit of the hill.
2. Mom left muffins in his lunchbox.
3. Tim will come dressed as a goblin.
4. Rocks hit the bottom of the pit.
5. Fred held a puppet on his hand.
6. A rabbit jumped into the basket.

7. Will you come to a picnic lunch?
8. The button matched the fabric.
9. Tom's kitten lapped up the milk.
10. Did the crash happen here?
11. I was absent from the lesson.
12. A ribbon on the bonnet fell off.

VC´/CV Words – Final y

1. poppy   sissy   filly
    tally   dolly   penny
    fifty   happy   sixty
    daddy   taffy   rally

2. angry   empty   pansy
    entry   pantry   plenty
    Henry   Sally   Molly
    Kenny   Billy   Bobby

VC/CV´ Words

3. until   upset   admit
    misled   pastel   unzip
    commit   indent   attend

1. Is there plenty of taffy?
2. Sally's back pantry was empty.
3. Daddy handed a penny to Bobby.
4. Molly is happy with the dolly.
5. You cannot go until I help you.
6. Mrs. Smith was upset and angry.

Practice

1. His stocking hung on the mantel.
2. Did you indent when you printed?
3. It is Dad's custom to fish here.
4. The tot did a simple puzzle.
5. Jim filled a basket with apples.

6. Can you drink a gallon of milk?
7. Fred said that the helmet was his.
8. Set the ham in the plastic dish.
9. Kenny can't unzip his backpack.
10. Mr. Black went to the dentist.

11. A possum hung from the branch.
12. Six lads pitched the canvas tent.
13. There are fifty maps in the atlas.
14. Stan has big boxes in his attic.
15. The velvet cloth felt soft.

16. Did you look for the lost mitten?
17. Bob kept the napkin in his lap.
18. Dogs and cats are mammals.
19. Mrs. Henry has on a pastel dress.
20. I am cutting the little pansy.
21. Are there sixty men in the band?

VC/CCV and VCC/CV Words

1. address   instant   pilgrim
    mattress   district   constant
    instruct   subtract   misspell

2. pumpkin   Franklin   illness
    helpless   transmit   endless

V<u>r</u>/<u>r</u>V

3. carry   marry   Larry
    Harry   tarry   berry
    merry   ferry   Jerry
    Kerry   Terry   sorry
    hurry   furry   curry

4. parrot   barren   errand
    horrid   carrot   torrent
    derrick   barrel   cherry

1. There is not such an address.
2. Can you subtract six from ten?
3. Tom cut the top off his pumpkin.

Mixed Practice

1. Can I catch the next ferry here?
2. Larry sells patches at camp.
3. Look at the blackberry in the dish.
4. The rabbit had a carrot to carry.
5. He was sorry Kerry didn't come.

6. The barrel fell off the truck.
7. Jan picked up the furry kitten.
8. Can you run an errand with Dad?
9. Mrs. Lang's hat has a red cherry.
10. The parrot said he has a cracker.

11. Tom cut his leg on a cactus.
12. The cat jumped into the sandbox.
13. Kenny can't handle a frisky dog.
14. His raft is drifting in the wind.
15. Look at the messy desk he left.

16. Henry hummed the long song well.
17. Dan grilled the ham on the rack.
18. Let's pack the trunk quickly.
19. There are six matches in the box.
20. In the huddle Rob planned a pass.
21. Molly and Jan giggled as he fell.

Open Long Vowels

1.	a	he	we	me
	be	the	she	hi
	I	no	go	so

2.	a	he	we	me
	am	hem	wet	men

3.	be	the	she	hi
	beg	them	shed	hip

4.	I	no	go	so
	it	nod	got	sob

Long Vowel y (ī)

5.	by	my	cry	dry
	fly	shy	why	sky
	try	fry	sly	pry

1. She met the shy lad at camp.
2. I am so glad to be with you.
3. Will you dry that dish in my sink?
4. Did his hat fly off in the wind?

Long a-consonant-e

1. same   came   game   tame
   name   fame   lame   dame

2. cake   take   make   bake
   lake   wake   sake   fake

3. rate   mate   hate   gate
   ate   fate   date   late

4. sale   male   pale   Dale
   lane   pane   cane   mane
   pave   wave   gave   save
   wade   made   fade   bade

5. shake   flake   snake   stake
   brave   slave   shave   crave
   frame   blame   flame   shame

1. Tape the red string on the gift.
2. Are there snakes in that cave?
3. Gale gave a date cake to us.
4. I will take a case of soft drinks.
5. We ate lunch in the shade.

Long <u>a</u>-consonant-<u>e</u>

1.   case   tale   vase   gaze
     safe   Kate   Jake   maze

2.   blade   whale   spade   skate
     plate   chase   blaze   trade
     stale   quake   state   brake

3.   rat   mad   can   tap
     rate   made   cane   tape

4.   pal   hat   Sam   fad
     pale   hate   same   fade

5.   cape   pan   mate   tam
     cap   pane   mat   tame

1. Jake went to the rink to skate.
2. The lamp and vase are on sale.
3. The tame cat sat in my lap.
4. Did you lock the gate to the path?
5. Sam runs to base and is safe.
6. A brave man shot the whale.
7. I will try not to be late.

Long i-consonant-e

1. like   bike   hike   Mike
   five   dive   live   hive
   ride   wide   side   tide
   line   fine   nine   dine

2. time   lime   dime   chime
   tire   wire   hire   size
   wise   rise   fire   prize

3. bride   glide   pride   slide
   crime   grime   slime   prime
   white   quite   sprite   spite
   shine   spine   whine   smile

4. bit   pin   rip   Tim
   bite   pine   ripe   time

5. dime   kit   wine   slid
   dim   kite   win   slide

1. We went on a bike ride by a lake.
2. Tim was so glad to win the prize.
3. When is it time to wake up?

Long o-consonant-e

1.
rode	joke	bone	vote
hole	rope	poke	code
more	nose	robe	woke
zone	home	coke	pose

2.
hope	dome	mole	wore
rose	pole	tote	doze
cone	mope	sore	yoke
bore	tone	hose	lone

3.
stove	shone	those	choke
quote	chore	stole	drove
close	globe	broke	store

4.
slope	smoke	chose	score
snore	grove	stone	froze

5.
glob	hope	rod	not
globe	hop	rode	note

1. The smoke from the blaze is thick.
2. The quake broke the glass panes.
3. We lost the game by a close score.

53

Short and Long Vowel Words

1. | grip | same | slap | slope |
    |------|------|------|-------|
    | blade | plod | limp | wire |
    | close | shy | flake | fact |
    | slid | mope | blot | blaze |

2. | cake | dim | snore | drab |
    |------|------|-------|------|
    | soft | tone | skim | gaze |
    | while | drop | grape | grid |
    | yoke | crab | slide | clog |

3. | shone | fry | milk | quake |
    |-------|------|------|-------|
    | plan | life | rose | whisk |
    | clot | bore | brake | task |
    | drive | rate | bond | zone |

1. Fry the eggs in the hot pan.
2. A crab will hide in the sand.
3. Five tots slid on the slide.
4. Dale likes to drink skim milk.
5. We ate a bunch of grapes at lunch.
6. The twins wore the same dress.
7. Set the white rose in the vase.
8. Did you drive at a fast rate?

Long <u>u</u>-consonant-<u>e</u> (ū)

1. mule   use   cure   fume
    cute   pure   fuse   mute

Long <u>u</u>-consonant-<u>e</u> (o͞o)

2. rule   June   rude   Luke
    lute   flute   lure   prune

Long (ū) or (o͞o)-consonant-<u>e</u>

3. tune   duke   tube   dude

4. cut   use   cube   tub
    cute   us   cub   tube

1. I smell the fumes from the truck.
2. Can you take a ride on a mule?
3. A flute has a soft tone.
4. There are nine prunes in the box.
5. Is it rude to yell in class?

Long e-consonant-e (ē)

here	Pete	eve	mere
	these	theme	

Mixed Practice

1.
pole	whine	snake	mute
gate	chore	prize	these
spike	brave	globe	cure

2.
state	rude	fire	quote
prime	brake	close	here
whale	smile	pure	froze

3.
cute	choke	skate	pride
theme	shave	wire	store
spine	prune	vote	blade

1. Come here and sit by the fire.
2. The bride wore a white dress.
3. Pete came to the game with me.
4. Is there a coke to drink?
5. Those soft rag dolls are cute.

-are (ār)

dare	care	hare	rare
mare	bare	fare	spare
share	glare	scare	stare

Add Learned Words: <u>for, have, what</u>

1. A hare ran in a hole by the rock.
2. Mom drove home from the store.
3. We have dimes for the bus fare.
4. My chore is to dry the plates.
5. A spare tire is in the trunk.

6. What is the name of that mare?
7. A flag was on top of the pole.
8. Mike and Tim can share the desk.
9. Will you care if I am late?
10. Use a blade to cut the rope.

11. Tom had a flat tire on his bike.
12. A cube has six sides.
13. Is there a cure for the mumps?
14. A duke sat next to the king.
15. What has the shape of a square?

C(s) before e, i, or y

1.
cent	cell	cinch	cite
rice	face	ice	lace
ace	nice	space	price

2.
mice	race	twice	place
grace	slice	pace	dice
spice	brace	splice	trace

3.
cost	cent	cinch	catch
ace	act	lace	last
dice	duck	ranch	race
track	trace	slice	slick

* * * * * * * * * * * * *

4.
cit	com	cest	caf
cel	cin	cos	cept
cris	cess	tric	fice
cide	col	cere	cile

1. She fell twice on the slick ice.
2. The track race had a swift pace.
3. What is the cost of a box of rice?
4. The lace on the dress is nice.
5. Can she trace the shape in ink?

V-consonant-e Compound Words

1. sunrise   handshake   rosebud
    pancake   tadpole   milkshake
    homesick   fireside   backbone
    grapevine   pothole   drugstore

2. inside   neckline   bathrobe
    hemline   flagpole   classmate
    snakeskin   sidestep   lifetime
    shipmate   homeland   brakeman

3. handmade   fireplug   hitchhike
    yuletide   sunshade   flashcube
    lineup   lifelong   smokestack

4. close-up   pinch-hit   drop-kick
    shut-in   nose-dive   trade-in
    self-made   mid-June   cave-in

1. Dad had six pancakes on his plate.
2. Kate drank a pink milkshake.
3. The lad was homesick at camp.
4. Kit wore a handmade bathrobe.
5. The sunshine felt hot on my back.

V-consonant-e + <u>ed</u> Suffix

The final <u>e</u> is dropped and the -<u>ed</u> added:

	<u>ed</u> (t)	<u>ed</u> (d)	<u>ed</u> (ĕd)
1.	piped	tamed	hated
	based	dined	voted
	hoped	used	sided
	hiked	tiled	faded
2.	shaped	closed	graded
	choked	whined	skated
	chased	blamed	noted
	sloped	shared	spaded
3.	biked	shamed	rated
	smoked	chimed	shaded
	baked	spared	crated

1. I choked on the pit in the prune.
2. We smoked a ham on the hot grill.
3. Hank skated on the thick ice.
4. Mom blamed me for the dented lamp.
5. He hated his grade on the quiz.

V-consonant-e + Consonant Suffix

1. safely   nameless   closely

    useful   wiseness   rudely

    lonely   hateful   soreness

2. wideness   bravely   rudeness

    scoreless   lateness   careless

    tameness   hopeless   lately

VC/CV Words with V-consonant-e

3. complete   admire   invite

    pollute   stampede   exhale

    arrive   entire   compose

    combine   explode   concrete

4. umpire   capsule   reptile

    costume   injure   baptize

    empire   dictate   trombone

1. The black witch costume scares me.
2. Did you invite Ed to come with us?
3. The lonely dog ate an entire bone.

Mixed VC/CV Words

1. citrus   cancel   fancy
   pencil   except   census
   accept   success   accent
   princess   advice   stencil

2. confuse   collide   ignore
   inhale   advise   inspire
   suppose   explore   oppose
   dispute   conclude   endure

Add Learned Words: <u>one</u>, <u>they</u>, <u>or</u>, <u>where</u>

1. Betty lost a pencil at the game.
2. Accept his advice with a smile.
3. Where are those states on a globe?
4. That's the last one of the chores.
5. Will Ted or Ben win the dispute?
6. They have asked for an umpire.
7. The princess wore a long dress.
8. She didn't arrive in time to rest.
9. Have you injured a leg by jumping?
10. The match was a scoreless one.
11. Is it a crime to pollute a lake?

<u>kind</u>-<u>old</u> Words

A word family where <u>i</u> has the long sound before two consonants:

1.	kind	find	mind	rind
	wind	hind	bind	grind

2.	wild	mild	child	pint

A word family where <u>o</u> has the long sound before two consonants:

3.	cold	mold	bold	sold
	told	hold	fold	old
		gold	scold	

4.	most	post	host	colt
	jolt	bolt	volt	molt

5.	roll	toll	poll	boll
	troll	scroll	stroll	both
		don't	won't	

1. A cold wind ended the long stroll.
2. His wild colt ran the most miles.
3. The blind man used a black cane.

63

y (ī)-consonant-e Words

type   style   Clyde   lyre

igh (ī) Words

1. high   sigh   thigh   might
   light   fight   right   tight

2. sight   fright   bright   slight
   night   plight   blight   flight

Compound Words with igh

3. midnight   sunlight   skylight
   nighttime   nightmare   spotlight
   flashlight   highland   upright

1. The child broke his right leg.
2. Clyde had a quick flight on a jet.
3. I can type a note if I have time.
4. A spotlight shone high in the sky.
5. Jane was scared by a nightmare.

ee (ē) Words

1. see   fee   bee   wee
    feet   beet   meet   seen
    need   weed   seed   feed
    deep   keep   beep   peep

2. week   peek   seek   jeep
    feel   heel   peel   reel
    beef   seem   deer   weep

3. free   glee   tree   three
    sheet   sleet   sweet   street
    greed   bleed   freed   speed
    sleep   creep   sheep   sweep

4. green   queen   screen   breeze
    steel   wheel   cheek   Greek
    teeth   speech   steer   freeze
    cheese   steep   cheer   squeeze

1. Lee will meet us by the tree.
2. Dad drove a jeep up a steep hill.
3. I need to sweep and mop next week.
4. The sheets will not dry in the sleet.

<u>ea</u> (ē) Words

1. | pea | sea | tea | flea |
    | eat | heat | beat | meat |
    | bean | mean | lean | Jean |
    | leak | beak | peak | weak |

2. | heal | seal | deal | meal |
    | beam | team | seam | veal |
    | leap | heap | leaf | bead |

3. | ear | fear | hear | dear |
    | near | tear | rear | gear |

4. | treat | pleat | cheat | wheat |
    | creak | sneak | speak | freak |
    | streak | squeak | steal | squeal |
    | steam | gleam | bleat | clean |

5. | each | beach | reach | peach |
    | teach | preach | bleach | leash |
    | cream | dream | stream | scream |
    | east | beast | least | yeast |

6. | clear | spear | smear | beard |
    | please | tease | leave | weave |

Mixed Practice

1. bet   red   pep   ten
    beet   reed   peep   teen

2. feel   step   sped   crept
    fell   steep   speed   creep

3. men   set   bed   met
    mean   seat   bead   meat

4. stem   beast   speck   plead
    steam   best   speak   pled

1. The sleet made the streets slick.
2. The queen gave a long speech.
3. Is it fun to sleep in a tent?
4. Did you see that tan deer leap?
5. We slept on the beach by the sea.
6. Can we have a treat for a snack?
7. Speak so that I can hear you.
8. Fred wore his jeans in the creek.
9. When is the next leap year?
10. I like to eat ice cream cones.
11. Eve ate a fresh peach with cream.

<u>oo</u> (o͞o) Words

1. moo   boo   too   zoo
   coo   woo   goo   Poo
   soon   moon   noon   food
   cool   tool   pool   fool

2. boot   hoot   toot   mood
   loop   hoop   poof   oops
   boom   room   doom   zoom

3. shoot   scoop   swoop   stoop
   droop   snoop   troop   brood
   stool   drool   spool   proof

4. bloom   groom   broom   gloom
   tooth   booth   roost   boost
   spoon   spook   smooch   smooth

5. goose   moose   loose   noose
   groove   choose   snooze   ooze

1. Tom lost his boot in the pool.
2. I need to clean my room soon.
3. What food do you eat at noon?

68

oo (o͝o) Words

1. book   hook   look   took
    cook   good   hood   wood
    wool   nook   poor   moor
    shook   crook   brook   stood

2. look   hod   shock   crook
    lock   hood   shook   crock

oo (o͞o) or (o͝o) Words

3. roof   root   hoof   soot
              hoop   coop

4. hoop   rot   coop   sod
    hop   root   cop   soot

1. Mom and Don are good cooks.
2. Look at the rocks in this brook.
3. Dad dug up the roots of the tree.
4. Can you twist and jump in a hoop?
5. The wind shook the wood roof.
6. Ted stood near the hen coop.

<u>ai</u> (ā) Words

1. rain   main   pain   gain
    aid   raid   maid   paid
    fail   pail   sail   mail

2. tail   rail   jail   hail
    aim   wait   bait   laid
    air   hair   fair   pair

3. train   brain   drain   grain
    plain   stain   sprain   chain
    faint   paint   saint   quaint

4. trail   snail   quail   frail
    claim   waist   faith   braid
    stair   chair   raise   praise

Add Learned Words: <u>do</u>, <u>two</u>, <u>who</u>

1. You must wait to claim the prize.
2. Rain and hail fell on the crops.
3. Who will use a fly for bait?
4. The train came to a stop at last.
5. She paid a lot for two long chains.
6. Do the pains make him cry?

Mixed Practice

1. pan lad pal bat
   pain laid pail bait

2. am paint clam braid
   aim pant claim Brad

3. ran pad main Stan
   rain paid man stain

4. reap aim droop reel
   glee noon wail seat
   took feet beast plain
   drain lean heel boost

5. leaf main sweet pool
   wood wheel proof saint
   trail scream brook speech
   three smooth pair beard

1. Sam claims that he reads books fast.
2. The tail of the goose fans the air.
3. Do you raise hens to sell?
4. Who went to jail for the crime?

<u>ay</u> (ā) Words

1. | day | pay | gay | lay |
   | may | way | hay | ray |
   | say | jay | Fay | bay |

2. | gray | tray | pray | stray |
   | play | clay | stay | sway |

3. | pay | lay | ray | may |
   | pail | laid | rain | mail |

4. | plain | tray | stair | spray |
   | play | trail | stay | sprain |

1. I will paint the room green.
2. Which way did the quail fly?
3. The lad ran up the steep stairs.
4. Did the rain fill the two pails?
5. Fay can braid the hair on a doll.
6. Dan sprays the grass with a hose.
7. The maid did not clean the stain.
8. Who made loops with the clay?
9. Set the stool by the gray chair.
10. Do rope belts stay on his waist?

oa (ō) Words

1. boat goat coat oats
    oak   soak road toad
    moan loan   Joan soap

2. coal goal foal   load
    foam roam loaf   coax
    oar   roar   soar hoax

3. boast roast coast toast
    coach roach poach oath
    groan cloak float   throat
    croak board hoarse coarse

4. got   rod   sock cot
    goat road soak coat

5. cloak cost   Tod   toast
    clock coast toad toss

1. We sailed on a boat to the coast.
2. His wheel hit a toad in the road.
3. Tod is hoarse with a sore throat.
4. Is there a load on the coal train?

oe (ō) Words

toe	hoe	doe	Joe
foe	woe	goes	toes

ow (ō) Words

1.

row	low	tow	bow
sow	mow	crow	grow
flow	blow	slow	glow
show	snow	stow	throw

2.

own	flown	grown	shown
blown	thrown	bowl	growth

1. The glass bowl broke in the sink.
2. Who will row the boat in the rain?
3. The west winds will blow the snow.
4. My pot roast has grown cold.
5. Use a hoe to dig up the weeds.
6. The slow snail crept up the trail.
7. Do black crows have ten toes?
8. Kites are flown in the spring.
9. Who goes to sleep at nine?

ou (ou) Words

1. out   pout   bout   gout
   scout   spout   trout   shout
   loud   proud   cloud   foul

2. noun   found   sound   wound
   round   pound   hound   bound
   mound   ground   count   bounce

3. ouch   couch   pouch   grouch
   slouch   crouch   mouth   south

4. our   sour   flour   scour
   blouse   house   mouse   ounce

5. pot   shot   clod   bond
   pout   shout   cloud   bound

1. I found a round stone that shines.
2. Do you shout when you see a mouse?
3. A long rain will soak the ground.
4. Our house is gray with green trim.
5. Who can count clouds in the sky?
6. Did Joe catch trout in the brook?

<u>ow</u> (ou) Words

1. how   now   cow   bow
   wow   brow   plow   vow

2. owl   fowl   howl   scowl
   growl   prowl   crowd   chow

3. down   gown   town   brown
   drown   clown   frown   crown

4. not   cob   how   crop
   now   cow   hot   crowd

Add Learned Words: <u>want</u>, <u>four</u>, <u>give</u>, <u>were</u>

1. The four clowns wore face paint.
2. The men in the crowd were freed.
3. A dog on a leash may growl.
4. I will give you a brown wool coat.
5. Do you want to clean my room now?
6. The queen wore a crown and a robe.
7. He wants to rent a booth at a fair.
8. A gray owl stays in the oak tree.
9. The bow of the ship sank in the sea.

<u>aw</u> (au) Words

1. | saw | paw | raw | jaw |
    | law | claw | flaw | slaw |
    | draw | straw | thaw | squaw |

2. | dawn | lawn | fawn | yawn |
    | pawn | drawn | hawk | squawk |
    | crawl | shawl | drawl | sprawl |

<u>au</u> (au) Words

haul	maul	Paul	taut
fault	vault	haunt	sauce
launch	cause	pause	gauze

1. A brown hawk can swoop down on it.
2. It is fun to drink with a straw.
3. You must not yawn when you speak.
4. Paul can draw what he wants.
5. Spooks haunt the old gray house.
6. What is the cause of such pain?
7. There is a flaw in this cloth.
8. Do not crawl in a tight space.

<u>al</u> (aul) Words

1. all   ball   fall   wall
    call   hall   tall   small

2. salt   malt   halt   Walt
    bald   scald   false   waltz

3. flow   screen   blouse   pleat
    vault   crown   sprain   false
    faint   sway   squaw   cheek
    cloud   freak   stow   praise

4. glee   bald   prowl   booth
    snow   mount   halt   quaint
    brook   preach   blown   cause
    wall   crowd   stray   toast

1. Waltz down the hall to our room.
2. Did you call to that bald man?
3. I like salt on my green beans.
4. Hot tea can scald if it spills.
5. When do leaves fall from trees?
6. A malt shop is near here.

oy (oi) Words

boy	joy	toy	soy
coy	Roy	Troy	Floyd

oi (oi) Words

1.
oil	foil	soil	boil
toil	coil	broil	spoil
coin	join	point	voice
void	noise	joint	choice
	moist	hoist	

2.
cot	job	toy	con
coy	joy	top	coin

3.
coal	join	nose	soil
coil	Joan	noise	sole

1. Troy spent his coins on a toy.
2. Who just made that loud noise?
3. It is not nice to point at me.
4. What choice of games do we have?
5. Who will plant seeds in the soil?

Vowel Digraph + Suffix

1.
freely	bleeding	sleepy
seemed	keeper	peeked
sweetly	speeded	weekly
meeting	deeply	cheered

2.
heater	clearing	neatly
creaked	peachy	feasting
nearer	treated	beater

3.
hooting	gloomy	cooled
smoothly	drooped	roomy
scooted	looping	brooms
cooker	hooking	looked

4.
plainly	failing	rainy
braided	quaintly	drained
aiming	mailed	fairly
paying	gayly	swayed

1. The men were sleeping on creaky beds.
2. Where is a roomy home to rent?
3. Mr. Green painted the steep stairs.
4. We cooked Greek treats for the fair.

Vowel Digraph + Suffix

1. groaning   soapy   toaster
   floated   coaster   foamy
   croaked   boarding   moaned

2. blower   snowy   slowly
   glowed   bowling   showy
   owning   mower   crowed

3. counting   roundly   scouted
   soured   pouting   cloudy
   founder   grouchy   slouched

1. He seemed to be pouting a lot.
2. On snowy days we are not grouchy.
3. Boats were floating on the lake.
4. Mrs. Browning boarded the plane.
5. The sled coasted down the slope.
6. Tell me what that groaning means.
7. The round moon glowed in the east.
8. Where is the lawn mower you found?
9. Who is the founder of this town?
10. Mr. Coats slowly went home to eat.
11. The leader was scouting for deer.

Vowel Digraph + Suffix

1.
crowded	plowed	clowning
prowler	howling	drowned
frowning	scowled	brownest

2.
clawing	pawned	scrawny
drawer	yawning	crawled
paused	jaunty	launched
halted	falsely	called

3.
toying	spoiled	pointed
oily	moistly	broiling
coined	toiling	jointly

1. I broiled beef chops on the grill.
2. We are counting the days to summer.
3. The boys called from the booth.
4. A prowler broke into my drawer.
5. We halted when the wind howled.
6. He is going into the crowded room.
7. Scowling means you are not happy.
8. The teacher didn't like clowning.
9. He crawled into bed since he was yawning each time he spoke.

Compound Words

1. beehive   deerskin   weekend
   treetop   seasick   mealtime
   leapfrog   teapot   seashore
   teacup   peanut   streamline

2. teaspoon   bedroom   toothbrush
   moonbeam   toothpick   broomstick
   fishhook   footstep   bookcase
   cookbook   woodshed   textbook
   footstool   scrapbook   footrest

3. mailman   pigtail   airplane
   raindrop   sailfish   mailbox
   haircut   waistline   upstairs
   airsick   hailstone   hairpin

1. The raindrops became hailstones.
2. We had a cleanup in the classroom.
3. At mealtime she used a toothpick.
4. I hear footsteps in my bedroom.
5. Joy had a haircut last weekend.
6. We found shells on the seashore.
7. Joe saw a beehive in the treetop.

Compound Words

1. railway   daytime   subway
   haystack   runway   plaything
   driveway   playmate   pathway

2. oatmeal   tugboat   seacoast
   toadstool   railroad   sailboat
   cockroach   lifeboat   blackboard
   roadside   coastline   billboard

3. tiptoe   toehold   doeskin
   toenail   showboat   snowdrift
   snowflake   scarecrow   rowboat

4. outfit   without   roundup
   outline   outgrow   background
   southwest   southeast   playground
   downtown   cowshed   cowskin

1. Bring the sacks to the stairway.
2. The boys played in the snowdrift.
3. Mr. Jones drives the bus downtown.
4. The scarecrow was made of straw.
5. Where is the moon in the daytime?

Compound Words

1. outlaw   seesaw   sawdust
   coleslaw   forepaw   crawfish
   jawbone   sawmill   rawhide

2. jigsaw   baseball   ballroom
   softball   football   smallpox
   snowball   hallway   launchpad

3. cowboy   tomboy   topsoil
   pinpoint   oilcan   pointblank

Add Learned Words: <u>some</u>, <u>put</u>, <u>know</u>, <u>any</u>

1. Some kids played on the seesaw.
2. Our team lost the baseball game.
3. Do you have any jigsaw puzzles?
4. Four boys had a snowball fight.
5. Where did Paul put the softball?
6. Tim wore his cowboy hat and boots.
7. What is smaller than a pinpoint?
8. The sawdust made me sneeze.
9. Who knows how to kick a football?
10. Hang the coats in the hallway.

VCCV Words

1. coffee   fifteen   sixteen
   indeed   appear   leaflet
   seamstress childhood   booklet

2. raccoon   shampoo   tattoo
   igloo   monsoon   mushroom
   balloon   pontoon   bamboo

3. maintain   explain   complain
   dainty   obtain   waitress
   Sunday   display   essay

1. On Sundays we like to have picnics.
2. Bob spilled coffee on the dresser.
3. Red balloons were displayed from the rooftops of the store.
4. I will read the booklet on plants.
5. Do not complain if the waitress appears to be frowning.
6. She is now sixteen years old.
7. Can you explain why the boy failed the test he took?
8. This leaflet makes a lot of sense.

VCCV Words

1.
pillow	yellow	shallow
minnow	hollow	fellow
follow	elbow	window
borrow	narrow	sparrow

2.
county	council	account
announce	countess	compound
applaud	laundry	applause
Austin	walnut	always
also	almost	walrus

3.
appoint	invoice	ointment
employ	enjoy	annoy

Add Learned Words: <u>been</u>, <u>very</u>, <u>about</u>, <u>work</u>

1. You may use minnows to catch fish.
2. I have an account with that store.
3. Have you been to Austin lately?
4. They employ men who will work well.
5. Cows follow the path very slowly.
6. Make a payment on that invoice.
7. Can you hear the applause for Bill?

Open Vowel Digraph Words

1. weevil   feeble   needle
    beetle   measles   easy
    beagle   eagle   peacock

2. poodle   noodle   daily
    daisy   dairy   raisin
    August   awning   dawdle
    faucet   saucy   poison

Mixed Compounds

1. seaweed   highway   eardrum
    crossroad   steamboat   penthouse
    outwit   bowleg   crayfish
    withdraw   chairman   goodwill
    spearmint   driftwood   playtime

1. Roy likes raisins in his muffins.
2. My poodle's name is Daisy Fay.
3. He is very angry about getting the measles and missing the game.
4. It is not easy to work each day.

<u>er</u> (ẽr) Words

1.
her	fern	term	herd
jerk	verb	Herb	Bert
clerk	stern	perch	berth
nerve	serve	swerve	verse

2.
supper	better	pepper
offer	summer	mutter
rubber	butter	ladder
banner	hammer	copper

3.
dinner	upper	letter
holler	stammer	scatter
manner	pattern	slippers

4.
robber	drummer	jogger
winner	slimmer	trimmer
sadder	hotter	flatter
shutter	zipper	madder

1. Pass the salt and pepper to Bert.
2. The butter melted on my pancakes.
3. I like summer better than fall.
4. Joan said that the fern was hers.

<u>er</u> (ẽr) Words

1.
after	winter	number
silver	lumber	finger
center	sister	temper
under	enter	vesper

2.
Denver	cancer	rafter
fender	pester	Chester
shelter	whisker	whisper
chapter	blister	whether

3.
thunder	plaster	cinder
expert	whimper	splinter
hamster	panther	antler
tumbler	monster	lobster

Add Learned Words: <u>away</u>, <u>many</u>, <u>your</u>, <u>other</u>

1. How close is Denver to your home?
2. Dot has a splinter in her finger.
3. Did you read very many chapters in your monster book?
4. Put the dishes away after dinner.
5. My other sister is older than I am.

<u>er</u> (ẽr) Words

1.
herself	kernel	perfect
sherbet	thermos	person
verdict	mercy	concert
western	lantern	concern

2.
perfume	termite	mermaid
beaver	eager	bleachers
Easter	sneakers	tweezers
rooster	scooter	sooner

3.
counter	powder	launder
saucer	power	flower
tower	shower	lawyer

1. The teacher did not allow us to whisper at the concert.
2. Jo put the sneakers on by herself.
3. How many saucers do you need?
4. The other team was eager to sit on the bleachers near the band.
5. Easter always comes in the spring.
6. Her perfume smelled like flowers.
7. Oysters are found in shells.

<u>ur</u> (ûr) Words

1. | fur | blur | spur | purr |
    |-------|-------|-------|-------|
    | curl | hurl | turf | surf |
    | turn | urn | burn | churn |
    | curb | hurt | blurt | spurt |

2. | curd | burp | slurp | burnt |
    |--------|-------|--------|--------|
    | church | burst | burned | turned |
    | nurse | purse | curse | curve |

3. | burner | murder | turnip |
    |---------|--------|----------|
    | burlap | murmur | burden |
    | sturdy | curtsy | Thursday |
    | further | survive | surprise |

4. | turtle | purple | hurdle |
    |--------|---------|---------|
    | curdle | disturb | furnish |

1. A turtle crawled on the turf.
2. Mom lost her purse last Thursday.
3. A sunburn on your nose will hurt.
4. Do not hit the curb when you turn.
5. The surprise came in a sturdy box.
6. My sister likes to curl her hair.

ir (ûr) Words

1. sir   fir   stir   girl
    dirt   shirt   skirt   flirt
    bird   third   firm   first
    irk   quirk   twirl   swirl
    chirp   thirst   squirm   squirt

2. thirty   circus   sirloin
    circle   squirrel   skirmish
    stirrup   thirsty   confirm

3. birthday   thirteen   whirlwind
    birdhouse whirlpool birdbath

1. The zipper broke on my wool skirt.
2. Is thirteen your lucky number?
3. The girl wore a purple shirt.
4. Who can sing the first verse?
5. I went to a circus on my birthday.
6. Bert draws circles in the dirt.
7. There are thirty boys and girls in the third grade class.
8. A birdhouse hung in the fir tree.
9. Squirrels hide nuts for the winter.

<u>ar</u> (är) Words

1.
car	far	tar	jar
bar	mar	star	scar
ark	dark	mark	park
bark	lark	spark	shark

2.
arm	farm	harm	charm
art	part	cart	dart
smart	chart	start	mart
barn	yarn	harp	Mars

3.
hard	yard	card	sharp
scarf	dwarf	harsh	snarl
arch	march	carve	starve

Add Learned Words: <u>could</u>, <u>would</u>, <u>don't</u>, <u>again</u>

1. How far away from here is Mars?
2. Bart's car will not start again.
3. Who would enjoy going to the park?
4. My nice sister said that I could borrow her scarf.
5. Don't throw the ball too hard.
6. The kitten chased the yellow yarn.

<u>ar</u> (är) Words

1.
carpet	garden	market
target	farmer	barber
garland	harvest	garlic
marvel	scarlet	garment

2.
army	tardy	arctic
harness	varment	parcel
tarnish	darling	varnish
archer	partner	farther

3.
marble	sparkle	startle
charcoal	cartoon	crowbar
harpoon	cargo	cardboard
shipyard	archduke	barnyard

1. The darts almost hit the center of the target.
2. Arthur will join the army soon.
3. I will get a hammer and ladder at the hardware store.
4. A parcel came in a cardboard box.
5. One person came late to the party.
6. A bug crawled under the carpet.

<u>or</u> (ôr) Words

1. or   for   nor   cord
    born   corn   horn   worn
    fork   cork   pork   stork
    dorm   form   storm   thorn

2. port   fort   sort   sport
    short   York   north   forth
    torch   porch   scorch   scorn
              force   horse

3. corner   forget   hornet
    orbit   order   support
    border   morning   absorb
    forty   inform   organ

4. former   normal   afford
    forgave   enforce   shortcake
    airport   horseback shortstop
    popcorn   seaport   northeast

1. Do you hear thunder in the storm?
2. We look at cartoons each morning.
3. Turn north at the next corner.

Final Unaccented V<u>r</u> (ẽr)

Final unaccented <u>ar</u> syllable (ẽr) in multisyllable words:

1. collar   grammar   dollar
    burglar   cellar   beggar
    Oscar   mortar   hangar

2. mustard   blizzard   custard
    westward   forward   standard
    backward   buzzard   afterward

Final unaccented <u>or</u> syllable (ẽr) in multisyllable words:

3. actor   doctor   pastor
    tractor   error   terror
    sponsor   harbor   scissors

4. inventor   collector   instructor
    inspector   conductor   contractor

1. Call the doctor if she's ill.
2. The shirt cost ten dollars.
3. Put the apples in the cellar.

Multisyllable Words with V<u>r</u>

1. September   important   carpenter
    interrupt   butterfly   hamburger
    advertise   surrender   Switzerland
    informal   yesterday   intersect

2. different   currently   bordering
    assorted   marketing   harvested
    hammered   survived   disturbing
    numbering   forlornly   according

3. gardened   carpeting   confirming
    surprised   perfectly   sponsoring
    personal   murmuring   concerning

1. We were disturbed by the sounds of the approaching blizzard.
2. The houses are numbered eastward.
3. A burglar broke a window in the cellar and caused terror upstairs.
4. They had hamburgers and assorted chips and garnishes to eat.
5. Yesterday was an important day.
6. That loud noise surprised us.

g before e̲, i̲, or y̲

Common Words with g (g) before e̲, i̲, or y̲:

1. | get | give | gift |
    | gear | girl | finger |
    | longer | stronger | hunger |
    | hanger | stinger | linger |

g is usually (j) before e̲, i̲, or y̲:

2. | gem | gent | ginger |
    | germ | gentle | German |
    | gin | gist | gym |

3. | age | page | rage |
    | cage | stage | wage |
    | fringe | hinge | singe |
    | huge | plunge | lunge |

1. Be gentle when playing with the German shepherd puppy.
2. The actor on the stage showed that he understood his part.
3. Do you like ginger in hot tea?

g (j) before e̲, i̲, or y̲

1. urge   merge   large
    barge   bulge   surge
    charge   verge   gorge

2. lounge   gouge   merging
    urgent   plunger   margin

Final -age̲ (ĭj) in multisyllables:

3. package   bandage   luggage
    rummage   scrimmage   baggage

Suffix -es̲ (ĕz) after g:

4. wages   lunges   hinges
    ages   charges   pages
    urges   bulges   stages

A family of ange̲ (ānj) words:

5. range   change   strange
    ranger   changer   stranger
    manger   danger   angel

V′/CV Words

1. o pen   ti ger   e ven
    gra vy   stu dent   ba sin
    sto ry   lo cate   si lent
    he ro   va cant   fe ver

2. la zy   ho ly   tu lip
    du ty   o ver   ba by
    lo cal   hu man   qui et
    su per   fro zen   ba con

3. spi der   u nit   bro ken
    to tal   gro cer   mi nus
    ro bot   na vy   spi ral
    pu pil   spo ken   mu sic

1. I like to eat bacon, eggs, and toast for supper on Fridays.
2. Can you help me locate a vacant house to rent until next March?
3. Each student must bring a spiral notebook to spelling class.
4. The teacher told a story of a local hero who saved a small child.

V´/CV Words

1.　fever　　　student　　story
　　even　　　tiger　　　locate
　　gravy　　　open　　　vacant
　　basin　　　silent　　hero

2.　over　　　baby　　　super
　　local　　　frozen　　holy
　　quiet　　　tulip　　　duty
　　human　　　lazy　　　bacon

3.　navy　　　minus　　　robot
　　spider　　broken　　pupil
　　grocer　　spiral　　unit
　　total　　　music　　　spoken

1.　It is his duty to call for help when a human life is at risk.
2.　What kind of music will be played at the student dance?
3.　The baby had a fever this morning.
4.　The grocer told us our total bill.
5.　Nine minus three is always six.
6.　Keep silent if you cannot be kind.

V´/CV Words

1. fiber   slogan   pilot
    ruby   basic   cement
    item   evil   florist
    radar   minors   private
    zero   polo   veto

2. clover   tiger   stupid
    jury   iris   recent
    rotate   profile   donate
    virus   Friday   cupid
    female   license   finance

3. vocal   oval   plural
    fatal   legal   penal
    label   siren   crazy
    diver   motor   silence
    Venus   Irish   Roman

1. Do you rotate tires each year?
2. The pilot of our airplane was the winner of the contest.
3. He lost his sister in a recent fatal car crash.

Vowel + C<u>le</u>

1. table   bugle   noble
    idle   able   Bible
    cradle   title   cable
    rifle   gable   maple
    fable   ladle   trifle

2. title   stable   bugle
    little   babble   juggle

    idle   rifle   bridle
    middle   ruffle   riddle

3. wiggle   rattle   table
    noble   huddle   title
    baffle   idle   settle
    cradle   pebble   fiddle

Add Learned Words: <u>pull</u>, <u>full</u>, <u>only</u>, <u>live</u>

1. The stable is full of hay.
2. I can only shoot a rifle well.
3. The horse will pull the cart if you put a bridle on him.

VC<u>e</u> + Vowel Suffix

1. | | | |
   |---|---|---|
   | fading | whiter | noted |
   | driver | smoking | ruler |
   | cutest | waded | chiming |
   | chosen | diving | wader |

2. | | | |
   |---|---|---|
   | griping | later | filed |
   | gripping | latter | filled |
   | | | |
   | tapped | robing | cutter |
   | taped | robbing | cuter |

3. | | | |
   |---|---|---|
   | dimmed | dated | spitting |
   | tiled | jobber | riding |
   | bitter | gaping | kidding |
   | hater | rubbing | raced |

1. A bell chimed loudly at two.
2. The bird was gliding in the gentle breeze.
3. The house we now live in has a pink tiled bathroom.
4. The noble ruler wore a crown.
5. My red robe faded on my shirt.

V/CV′ Words

1. began   begin   begun
    below   because   belong
    beside   behave   behind
    became   before   beware
    besides   betray   between

2. return   repair   repeat
    remain   refer   recite
    require   recall   refuse
    resume   reduce   reform
    rejoice   retreat   relax

3. decay   decide   defeat
    desire   delight   defend
    depart   declare   decrease
    defense   define   defrost
    delay   demand   depend

1. Too much sweet food will soon cause teeth to decay.
2. The cattle belong to a student.
3. Did you decide to repeat the test before you depart?

V/CV´ Words

1. event   elect   erase
   evade   eject   elapse
   erect   erupt   evict

2. provide   produce   protect
   promote   propose   proceed
   proclaim   pronounce   protest

3. prevent   prefer   prescribe
   pretend   precook   predict
   prepare   present   preserve

4. unite   polite   omit
   hotel   motel   sedan
   secure   select   brunet
   deduct   retreat   o'clock

Add Learned Words: today, buy, once, pretty

1. The girls will provide pretty presents for the party.
2. Today I would like to buy my gift.
3. Once we stayed at a nice hotel.

<u>a</u>/CV´ and Final <u>a</u> Words

An <u>a</u> at the end of an unaccented syllable has the "obscure" (à) or "schwa" sound (ə).

1. along   ago   adopt
   alike   alone   awake
   adapt   alive   away

2. apart   alarm   about
   around   aboard   amount
   avoid   afraid   aloud

3. la pel´   sa lute´   ca reer´
   ca nal´   ma ture´   ba ton´
   pa rade´   ca det´   ma roon´

4. data   quota   tuba
   sofa   comma   extra
   momma   delta   plasma
   Linda   Carla   Rosa

1. The cadets will parade today.
2. They march along briskly.
3. Awards are on many lapels.

ĭ/CV´ Words

Short ĭ (ĭ) in open unaccented syllables:

1.   divide   divorce   dilute
      digest   divine   direct

2.   dif´ fi cult   ac´ ci dent
      as´ pi rin   es´ ti mate
      an´ ti dote   ter´ mi nate
      max´ i mum   con´ fi dent

3.   can´ di date   ver´ ti cal
      lon´ gi tude   lat´ i tude
      of´ fi cer   or´ di nance
      hur´ ri cane   in´ sti tute
      prac´ ti cal   ob´ li gate

1. Let's ventilate the room at once.
2. The principal told the students that they must make better grades.
3. Can you divide twenty by five?
4. Mr. Clay reported the accident.
5. Who is the best candidate to be mayor of Fort Collins?

Mixed Multisyllables

1. following   employment   installment
    afternoon   fingernail   underneath
    committee   understood   entertain
    establish   tenderloin   outstanding

2. as tro naut   boun da ry
    pet ti coat   o ver seas
    a part ment   Hal lo ween
    va nil la   e lec tric

3. e quip ment   e mer gen cy
    au to mat ic   ve hi cle
    pro hib i ted   sand wich es
    cus to mer   per ma nent

4. however   possible   children
    maximum   loitering   prohibit
    internal   gentlemen   admittance
    dynamite   employee   trespassing

1. A committee understood the problem.
2. The equipment is all automatic.
3. Parking there is prohibited.

Silent Consonants

Initial silent <u>k</u> in <u>kn</u>:

1.   knit   knot   knock   knee
       know   knight   knife   known
       kneel   knack   knead   knob
               knuckle   knickers

2.   knapsack   kneedeep   knothole
       knockout   jackknife   slipknot

Initial silent <u>w</u> in <u>wr</u>:

3.   wrap   wreck   wrist   wrong
       wring   write   wrench   wreath
       wrinkle   written   wrapper
       wrecked   writing   wrapped

1. The maiden knocked at the gate.
2. Her car was wrecked when a huge truck turned out into her path.
3. Did you hurt a knee when you fell?
4. He dropped the gum wrapper on the playground near the slide.

Silent Consonants

Final b in mb:

1. bomb   limb   dumb   lamb
   crumb   thumb   jamb   numb
   bomber   plumber

Kind-old words: climb   comb

Medial t:

2. listen   moisten   fasten
   often   soften   castle
   whistle   wrestle   bristle
   glisten   gristle   rustle

Silent l:

3. talk   walk   chalk   balk
   caulk   stalk   hălf   călf

1. A loud whistle sounded at noon.
2. Her thumb was numb from the blow.
3. A tall stalk sways in the breeze.
4. The princess slept in a castle.

<u>dge</u> (j) Words

1. fudge   badge   edge   dodge
   bridge   hedge   budge   ridge
   judge   ledge   nudge   dredge
   pledge   grudge   wedge   lodge

2. bug   brig   jug   log
   budge   bridge   judge   lodge

3. badge   smug   ledge   rig
   bag   smudge   leg   ridge

<u>dge</u> + <u>vowel</u> <u>suffix</u>

4. judges   lodges   ridges   badges
   wedges   budges   hedges   bridges

5. lodged   wedged   judged   dodged
   pledging   bridging   trudging

1. The lady had smudges on her nose.
2. Two green hedges lined the edges
   of Mrs. Winter's yard.
3. We played dodge ball after lunch.

VC´/V Words

1. sol id   lim it   hab it
   cam el   rob in   pan el
   sev en   cab in   sal ad
   clos et   prof it   tim id

2. rec ord   pres ent   tav ern
   ev er   vol ume   com ics
   pris on   pan el   proj ect
   riv er   cit y   spir it

3. atom   rapid   polish
   rigid   planet   finish
   body   modern   exit
   metal   credit   never

4. rather   liver   presence
   second   logic   adult
   taxi   radish   lozenge
   legend   tragic   frigid

1. Suck on a lozenge to make a sore throat feel better.
2. Do you read the comics daily?

VC´/V Words

1.
second	given	digit
level	linen	civil
pedal	tenant	comet
image	damage	manage

2.
kitchen	pocket	ticket
racket	chicken	locker
bucket	pitcher	cracker
ketchup	jacket	hatchet

3.
every	medical	Saturday
hospital	resident	register
property	restaurant	general
military	prosecute	benefit
elevator	poverty	president
several	parallel	family

1. The ambulance rushed the man to the nearest hospital.
2. Put the ketchup in the first cabinet in the kitchen.
3. A pocket of his jacket was damaged by the cleaners.

<u>ea</u> (ĕ) Words

1. | head | dead | lead |
    |------|------|------|
    | bread | read | death |
    | deaf | meant | dealt |
    | health | wealth | breath |

2. | dread | breast | thread |
    |-------|--------|--------|
    | sweat | threat | spread |
    | ready | heavy | steady |
    | heaven | weapon | weather |

3. | instead | leather | measure |
    |---------|---------|---------|
    | sweater | pleasant | treasure |
    | heading | feather | pleasure |
    | ahead | already | peasant |

4. | breakfast | headline | deadline |
    |-----------|----------|----------|
    | cornbread | breathless | deafness |
    | heavenly | threaten | wealthy |

1. My leather coat has brown thread.
2. Hunt for the hidden treasure.
3. Put on a thick sweater since the weather has turned cold.

<u>o</u> (ŭ) in Accented Syllable

1. | come | some | none | won |
   | done | ton | son | love |
   | front | month | dove | shove |

2. | mother | other | brother |
smother	another	Monday
cover	color	oven
dozen	shovel	wonder

3. | income | govern | nothing |
discover	company	recover
among	become	London
	government	monthly

Add Learned Words: <u>does</u>, <u>blue</u>, <u>their</u>, <u>laugh</u>

1. His brother lost his blue gloves.
2. Bill needed a compass and a shovel in the woods.
3. Fools laugh at their own jokes. Does Jane?
4. She wondered what the big company would do with it.

Common Word Groups

<u>wa</u> (wǒ) words:

1. | | | | |
    |---|---|---|---|
    | was | want | wad | watt |
    | swan | wand | wasp | swat |
    | watch | water | wander | wash |
    | swap | waffle | waddle | wallet |

<u>ey</u> (ē) words:

2. | | | |
    |---|---|---|
    | key | alley | valley |
    | kidney | donkey | monkey |
    | chimney | turkey | whiskey |
    | jersey | jockey | hockey |

<u>ew</u> (ū) or (o͞o) words:

3. | | | | |
    |---|---|---|---|
    | new | blew | grew | few |
    | chew | crew | drew | flew |
    | stew | threw | shrewd | screw |

4. | | | | |
    |---|---|---|---|
    | curfew | jewel | mildew | sewer |
    | Jewish | Lewis | Andrew | Stewart |
    | outgrew | newspaper | | withdrew |

-<u>tion</u> (shŭn) Words

1. nation   lotion   motion
   station   option   caution
   mention   section   action
   junction   auction   fraction

2. attention   induction   convention
   exemption   invention   objection
   taxation   location   promotion
   solution   selection   relation

3. addition   ignition   condition
   ambition   inspection   collection
   affection   edition   protection
   emotion   election   probation

1. Your tires need traction when ice collects on the highways.
2. This nation had a strong and lasting foundation.
3. What is Jill's condition now?
4. Take caution not to enter an intersection without looking.
5. Do they sell toys at an auction?

ABOUT THE AUTHORS

Dorothy B. Montgomery, MEd, has been a language, remedial, and reading specialist for more than twenty years in Wichita Falls, Texas. Having received a BA degree from the University of Texas, she began her teacher training with certification as a language therapist in the class with Carolyn Bowen, author of *Angling for Words,* at the Language Training Unit of Texas Scottish Rite Hospital in Dallas, Texas. She taught privately as a therapist before receiving teacher certification and entering public school teaching. She is the author of *Phono-Cards* and *The Teacher's Line* in the *Angling* series, which provided teachers in both public and private settings with a guide for using the program.

She was certified in Language/Learning Disabilities and received a master's degree in secondary education from Midwestern State University. She served six years as a high school resource teacher after four years of teaching remedial English and reading. Her certification as a reading specialist was earned in a second master's program. In 1979 she returned to private services and formed a partnership entitled Educational Service Associates with her two teacher daughters, one of whom, Linda M. Gipson, is co-author of this book. At the present time she practices as an educational therapist, reading specialist, and educational consultant in curriculum.

Professional awards have included being named Teacher of the Year by the Wichita Falls Classroom Teachers and Wichita Falls LDA and the Outstanding Teacher by the area Council for Exceptional Children. She has made numerous presentations at conferences and in-service workshops. Recently she has been active in guiding the formation of the Wichita Adult Literacy Council. Her professional activities also include Texas LDA, in which she served on the Professional Advisory Committee, Association of Educational Therapists, Delta Kappa Gamma, and the Orton Society.

Linda M. Gipson, MEd, received her BS degree in special education from the University of Houston and her master's degree from Midwestern State University, Wichita Falls, Texas. She earned four special education certifications and taught five years in Spring Branch and Wichita Falls schools as an elementary resource teacher before joining Educational Service Associates. Linda practices as a registered educational diagnostician, an educational therapist, and a curriculum consultant, with specialization in mathematics and reading.

She served as a consultant in the development of Project Guide II and Region IX Educational Service Center, Wichita Falls, Texas, and has given in-service and conference presentations on math disabilities. Awards include being named Elementary L/LD Resource Teacher of the Year by the Wichita Falls LDA for 1978-79 and to Outstanding Young Women of America. Her professional activities include LDA and Delta Kappa Gamma.